Fair
Phonics
D0674196
Brown Watson
ENGLAND

# Contents

# Let's have some fun with phonics!

These classic fairy tales have been retold with a twist, to help your children recognise and practise key sounds that they will be learning at school. Each story has a vowel sound highlighted in red, and a secondary consonant sound picked out in blue.
Read the stories together and point out the sounds in coloured text. Repeat them out loud and listen closely. Look at the different letters that can be used to make the key sounds – for example, the 'w' sound in wish and whale. Have fun thinking of other words that use the same sounds, and combine them to sound out new words.

Take it slowly, and stop when your child has had enough. You can still enjoy the stories and their colourful illustrations without focusing on the phonics. Soon your child will have discovered some timeless tales, and learned reading skills as they go.
**Enjoy your time together!**

# Red Riding Hood

Once there was a little girl who always wore a red cape with a hood to cover her head. Everyone called her Red Riding Hood.

'Your granny is not well,' said Red Riding Hood's mummy. 'Take this bread and these eggs and see if she needs any help.'

Red Riding Hood was deep in the forest when she stopped for a rest. 'Hello,' said a wolf. 'I don't think we've met?'

Red Riding Hood leapt up and fled. The wolf ran ahead and went straight to granny's house. 'Oh!' exclaimed granny as the wolf bundled her under the bed.

'Enter!' called the wolf and Red Riding Hood crept into the room. 'Mummy sent me,' she explained, 'to check that you're getting better.'

'Come nearer,' growled the wolf. 'I'm a little bit deaf.' Red Riding Hood leant closer. 'Granny!' she said. 'Your legs are all furry! And you smell really bad!'

The wolf leapt out of the bed. 'Help! Help!' begged Red Riding Hood. Two workmen looked in to see who was yelling.

The men grabbed a net, and held the wolf tightly inside. Red Riding Hood helped granny get up. They hugged each other and wept.

# Pinocchio

An old man worked hard making toys. He was happy, but he wished for a boy of his own. The next day, his little puppet started to move!

The man was overjoyed. He called the toy Pinocchio. A fairy told him, 'If you are good, I will turn you into a real boy.'

Pinocchio wanted to be a schoolboy like his friends. On the way to class, he heard lots of noise. It was a puppet show!

The theatre owner wanted Pinocchio to join his show. When Pinocchio cried, he gave him some coins and sent him home.

A wicked fox lied to Pinocchio. 'If you bury your coins in the soil, they will grow into a money tree.' Then he stole the buried coins.

Still Pinocchio did not learn. He followed some voices and visited Toyland. He was too busy enjoying himself to go home.

Pinocchio had a loyal friend called Jiminy Cricket. He said that Pinocchio's father had gone on a long voyage. He had been swallowed by a whale!

Pinocchio dived inside to rescue him. The whale coughed and spat them both out. 'You made a brave choice,' said the fairy. 'Now you will be a real boy!'

# The Wizard of Oz

The wind howled and swirled around Dorothy's house. It blew so hard it picked up her house and dropped it in the Land of Oz!

Dorothy and Toto went outside. 'You killed the wicked witch and now we are free!' shouted the Munchkins.

A kind witch appeared in the crowd. 'Take these magic slippers and follow the yellow brick road,' she said. 'Ask the Wizard to send you home.'

Dorothy walked down the road and met a scarecrow. He was sad because he had no brain. 'Ask the Wizard to help you out,' said Dorothy.

They went into the woods and found a man made of tin. He really wanted a heart. 'Come to see the Wizard,' announced Dorothy.

A lion roared loudly at them, but he was really as shy as a mouse. 'The Wizard can stop you being so cowardly,' they all agreed.

After many hours they reached the town. 'Wow!' they gasped. 'Look at those grand towers! The Wizard must be very powerful.'

The Wizard granted their wishes. 'But you have your own power,' he told Dorothy. 'Click your heels and count to three and you will soon be home.'

# Key Sounds

Say these words out loud. Which story are they from?
Listen for the sounds you have learned.

rest
room
furry
growled
forest

town
tin
heart
towers
granted